DIGESTING THE CHILD WITHIN

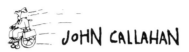 JOHN CALLAHAN

John Callahan is no ordinary cartoonist. Abandoned at birth by his mother, he was educated by Roman Catholic nuns with an emphasis on guilt and harsh discipline, he became an alcoholic by the age of 12 and was paralysed in a car accident shortly after his 21st birthday. It took six years of heavy drinking before Callahan got to realise that his problem was alcoholism and not quadriplegia. With his recovery, he returned to a childhood passion and started working hard on his cartoons. Callahan can't move all his fingers, so he draws by clutching a pen in his right hand and guiding it across the page with his left.

Now some fifteen years later, Callahan's work appears in over forty newspapers and his autobiography 'Don't worry, He won't get far on foot' has been published to critical and commercial success.

Published by Statics (London) Ltd
41 Standard Road, London NW10 6HF

Copyright © 1991 by John Callahan

Printed in England by H.P.H. Print Ltd.
8 Gorst Road, London NW10 6LE.

ISBN 1 - 873922 - 05 - 1

DIGESTING THE CHILD WITHIN

JOHN CALLAHAN

STATICS BOOKS

SHOOT-OUT AT THE SCHIZOPHRENIC CORRAL

CALLAHAN

"IT WAS HIM OR ME!"

CALLAHAN

"JENKINS, YOU'VE BEEN SPENDING FAR TOO MUCH TIME
AT THE WATER-COOLER!"

"SOMEDAY, SON, ALL THIS WILL BE YOURS!"

"MISS SHACKLY, PLEASE BRING ME A LARGER CHAIR."

"YOUR TABLE IS READY."

CALLAHAN

CALLAHAN

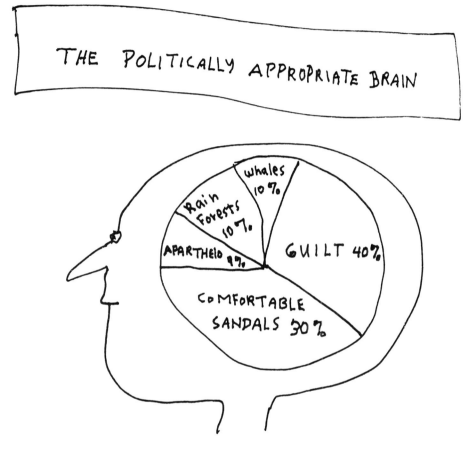

CALLAHAN

"... AND WE'VE ARRANGED A WINDOW SEAT FOR YOUR DOG
SO YOU CAN ENJOY THE VIEW!!"

CALLAHAN

"COULD BE A GOOD CAREER MOVE!"

"NOW, ISN'T THAT BETTER THAN THAT OLD CANNED LIVER?"

CALLAHAN

"LET'S TALK A LITTLE ABOUT THAT HOLLOW FEELING."

"IT DOESN'T SEEM LIKE CHRISTMAS WITHOUT SNOW!"

". . . AND I HAVE DIFFICULTY GETTING CLOSE TO PEOPLE . . ."

"EATING THE APPLE COULDN'T HAVE BOTHERED HIM THAT MUCH. IT MUST HAVE BEEN THE FACT THAT I FUCKED YOU."

MEN

MADMEN

CALLAHAN

"YES!! FOR THE HUNDRED AND FIFTIETH TIME! WE'RE
BURNING IN HELL!!!"

"I'LL HAVE WHAT I'M HAVING."

"NOW GET OUT THERE AND RAKE UP THOSE FALLEN LIMBS!"

CALLAHAN

"HELP! I'VE FALLEN AND I CAN'T GET UP!!"

"YOUR ORDER IS NOT READY, NOR WILL IT EVER BE."

"WELL, DARLING, IT LOOKS LIKE THE STARS HAVE FALLEN FROM
THE SKY, THE RIVERS HAVE ALL RUN DRY, AND THE POETS HAVE
RUN OUT OF RHYMES. GUESS I DON'T HAVE TO LOVE
YOU ANYMORE."

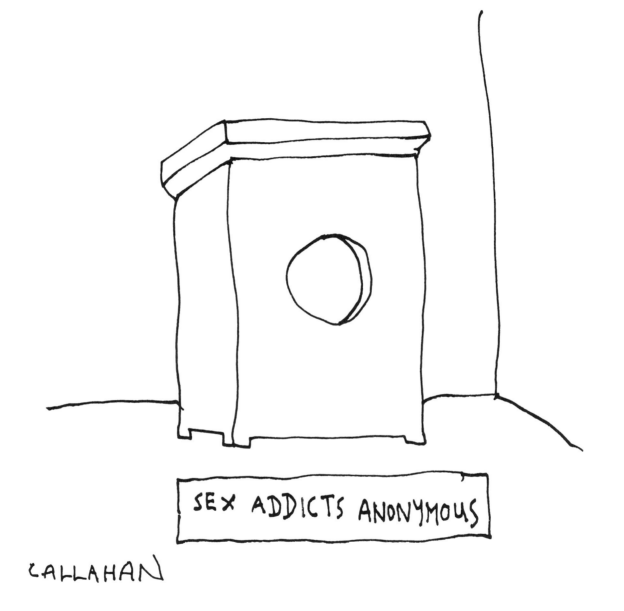

SEX ADDICTS ANONYMOUS

CALLAHAN

"YOU READ ABOUT THESE THINGS HAPPENING TO OTHER PEOPLE!"

"I DREAMT I HAD A HAREM, BUT THEY ALL WANTED TO TALK
ABOUT THE RELATIONSHIP."

HANNIBAL CROSSING HIS WIFE.

CALLAHAN

"I WONDER IF YOU'D MIND GIVING ME DIRECTIONS. I'VE
NEVER BEEN SOBER IN THIS PART OF TOWN BEFORE."

CALLAHAN

"FINISH YOUR VEGETABLES! THERE ARE CHILDREN IN
BEVERLEY HILLS WITH EATING DISORDERS."

CALLAHAN

"DADDY! YOUR BARN DOOR IS OPEN!"

CALLAHAN

"DAMMIT! I RESENT BEING TREATED AS IF I WERE SOBER!"

A.A. IN L.A.

CALLAHAN

"MY NAME IS MORT AND I REPRESENT CHUCK WHO'S AN
ALCOHOLIC."

"MISS JENKINS, PLEASE DIE."

RICHARD'S LONELINESS ONLY DEEPENED AFTER SYLVIA'S HELIUM BREAST IMPLANTS.

CALLAHAN